WOLFGANG AMADEUS MOZART
25 EARLY PIECES

Edited by Howard Ferguson

The K-numbers refer to the order shown in the 7th edition
of Köchel's Thematic Catalogue of Mozart's Works, 1965.

THE ASSOCIATED BOARD OF
THE ROYAL SCHOOLS OF MUSIC

INTRODUCTION

WOLFGANG AMADEUS MOZART
(27.1.1756 - 5.12.1791)

The 25 pieces in this album have been chosen from those composed by Mozart for harpsichord between the ages of five and nine. The earliest were written down for him by his father, Leopold, who doubtless allowed himself some discreet tidying-up; for several of the pieces in the later 'London Notebook' of 1784, written by Wolfgang himself when his father was ill during their visit to England, contain blatant ineptitudes that must give a truer picture of the child's ability, astonishing though it was.

The present texts are taken from photocopies of Leopold's MSS when the latter exist (Nos.1-6, 8, 9 & 11); from their earliest publication in Nissen's *Biographie W.A.Mozart's*, Leipzig 1828 (Nos.7 & 10); and (for Nos.12-25) from the 1st edition of the 'London Notebook' (*Mozart als achtjähriger Komponist*, ed. G.Schünemann; Breitkopf & Härtel, Leipzig 1908). Mozart's autograph of the latter, which disappeared from the Preussischer Staatsbibliothek, Berlin, during World War II, is now in the Biblioteka Jagiellónska, Kraków.

Numbered footnotes here deal with textual matters, and lettered footnotes with interpretation. A realization of each ornament is shown either above or below the stave on its first appearance in each piece, short appoggiaturas being indicated by a small ♪. Redundant accidentals have been omitted. All phrase-marks, other than those noted in footnotes, are editorial, as are the dynamics (for the use of pianists), tempo-marks, notes, accidentals, rests, etc., printed either small or within square brackets. Curved brackets indicate that a note should not be struck.

Thanks are due to the Mozarteum, Salzburg; the Museum Carolino Augusteum, Salzburg; the Stadtbibliothek, Leipzig; and the Mary Flagler Music Collection in the Pierpont Morgan Library, New York, for providing photocopies of respectively K.4 & K.5, K.1e & K.1f, K.3, and K.1a-K.1d, and for giving permission for them to be used in establishing the present texts.

HOWARD FERGUSON
Cambridge 1987

25 EARLY PIECES

Andante in C †
K.1a

MOZART

Early 1761

Allegro in C †
K.1b

† Mozart's father, Leopold, noted on the manuscript of Nos. 1 & 2: 'Some of young Wolfgang's compositions written during the first three months of his 5th year.'

1) B.4: the r.h. slurs are in the source.

AB 1983

Allegro in F

K.1c

11 December 1761

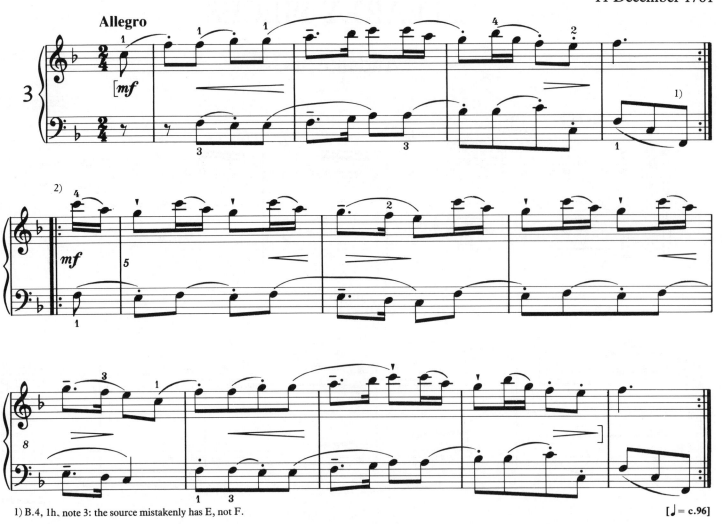

1) B.4, 1h, note 3: the source mistakenly has E, not F.

[♩ = c.96]

2) The staccato wedges and 2-note slurs in r.h. bb.4-7 & 10-11 are in the source. As was usual in the 18th century, the wedge implies a normal staccato, not a staccatissimo

Menuett in F

K.1d

16 December 1761

(a) Set the tempo by b.3, otherwise the opening is likely to be too fast.

1) B.3: the last two r.h. slurs are in the source; the remainder are editorial.

Menuett in G

K.1e

?1764

1) The crotchet slurs in bb.2, 4 & 10 are in the source.

[♩ = c.138]

AB 1983

Menuett in C

K.1f

?1764

1) The crotchet slurs in r.h. bb. 7-8, 10 & 12 are in the source.

[♩= c.132]

Menuett in F

K.2

January 1762

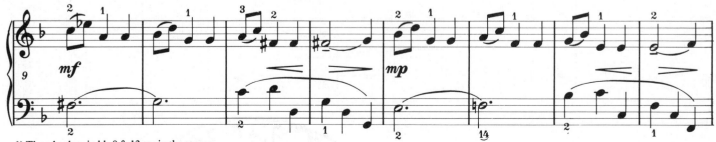

1) The r.h. slurs in bb.8 & 12 are in the source.

[♩ = c.126]

Allegro in B flat
K.3

4 March 1762

1) The r.h. slurs in bb.1, 7-8, 11, 13, 17, 21-22 & 29 are in the source.

2) B.29, l.h.: the source has two crotchets; but see the more probable b.11.

[♩ = c.116]

AB 1983

Menuett in F
K.4

11 May 1762

1) The staccatos and slurs in r.h. bb.5-7, 12, 14 & 19-22 are in the source.

$[\, \lefthalf = \text{c.108}]$

Menuett in F
K.5

5 July 1762

[♩ = c.108]

Allegro in C
K.5a

1) Bb.12-13 & 35-36: in the source the 1.h. semiquaver triplets are written thus: ♪ ♫, which was the correct contemporary notation for the present text. Most modern editions wrongly transcribe this as: ♪ ♪ ♫.

2) The slurs in r.h. b.39 and l.h. b.41 are in the source.

[♩ = c.92]

From the 'London Notebook', 1764-5

Menuett in A flat
K.15ff

[♩= c.104]

Andante in E flat
K.15mm

[♩= c.84]

1) B.8: the double-bar and repeats are editorial.
2) B.12: the source has a pause over the final crotchet. The D.C. is editorial.

AB 1983

Menuett in B flat

K.15pp

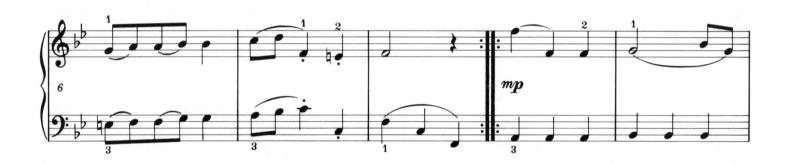

1) The 2-note slurs in r.h. b.5 are in the source.

[♩ = c.120]

AB 1983

Menuett in G

K.15c

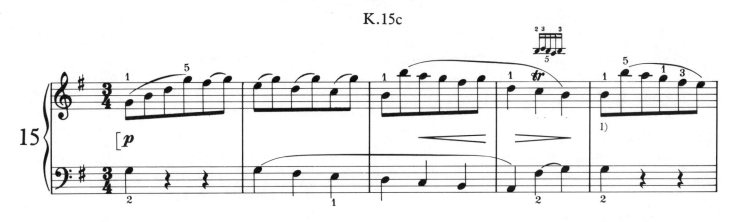

1) Bb.5-6, r.h. note 1: the source has G & C respectively.

2) B.17, r.h. note 1: the source has middle-C.

3) B.20, l.h. note 1: the source adds a lower G octave, which appears to be in a slip.

[♩ = c.100]

AB 1983

Contredance in G
K.15e

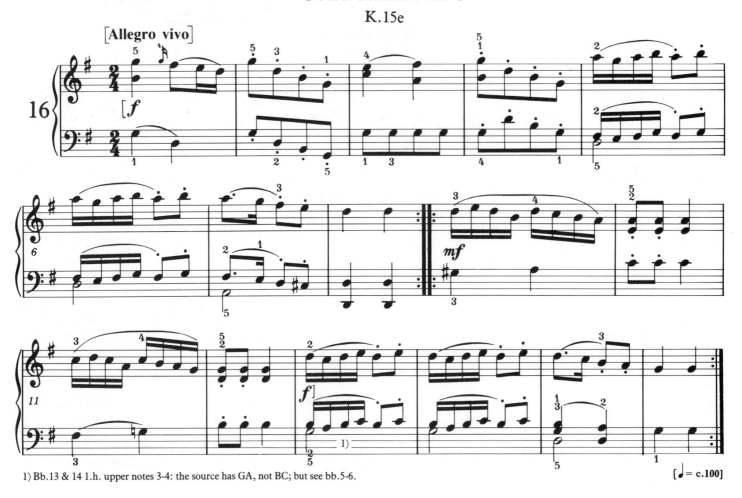

1) Bb.13 & 14 1.h. upper notes 3-4: the source has GA, not BC; but see bb.5-6.

[♩ = c.100]

Menuett in F
K.15oo

1) The crotchet slur in b.5 is in the source.

[♩ = c.138]

Presto in B flat

K.15 ll

1) The slurs and staccatos in r.h. bb.9-11 are in the source.

2) B.12, l.h. note 1: the source has F not G.

3) B.22, l.h. chord 1: the source has dotted-crotchets.

AB 1983

Adagio in D

K.150

1) In the source the upbeat to bb.1 & 14 is a crotchet; but the semiquaver upbeat to b.16 seems more in keeping with the prevailing rhythm.

2) B.11, r.h. lower line, notes 1 & 2: the source has demi-semiquavers placed a semiquaver later.

3) B.13: the source has r.h. crotchet and l.h.

4) B.22, final chord: the source has crotchets.

[♪ = c.54]

Rondo in F

K.15hh

1) B.38, l.h. note 1: the source has E, not C.

[♪ =c.132]

Andante in B flat

K.15ii

1) B.2, r.h. notes 2-4: the source has ♪♫ ; but see the more probable b.19.

2) B.27, r.h. notes 2-4: the source has three demi-semiquavers.
3) B.34, r.h.: the source has a dotted-crotchet chord.
4) B.38, r.h. note 2, lower line: in the source the G is a quaver on the 2nd quaver beat.

[♩ = c.76]

Rondo in D

K.15d

1) B.8, r.h. chord 1: the source adds a redundant G between B/E; also an unwanted barline after the 3rd quaver.

[♪ = c.168]

Menuett in F

K.15m

[♩ = c.112]

Andantino in C

K.15b

1) Bb.2 & 6, r.h. chord 1: the source has a D above the B.
2) B.4, r.h. note 2: the source has C, not D.
3) B.6, r.h. upper line notes 3-4: the source adds DC below FE; but see b.2.

[♪ = c.104]

AB 1983

Allegro in F
K.15a

1) In the source there are more staccatos and slurs in this piece than in any other found in the 'London Notebook'. As they are rather haphazardly placed, however, many of those shown above are editorial.

2) Bb.26 & 32 l.h.: the source has dotted crotchets, not quavers.

AB 1983

THEMATIC INDEX

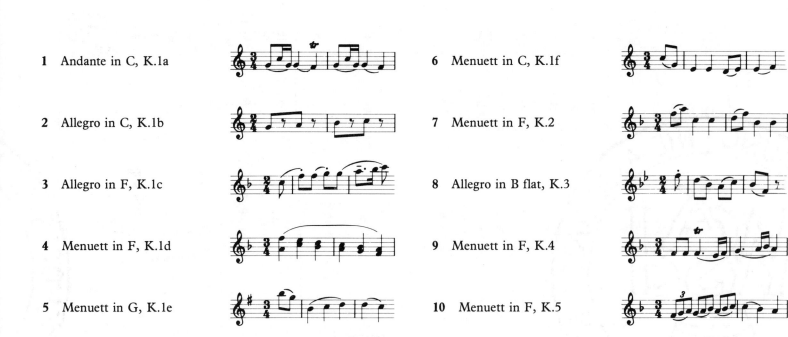

1 Andante in C, K.1a

2 Allegro in C, K.1b

3 Allegro in F, K.1c

4 Menuett in F, K.1d

5 Menuett in G, K.1e

6 Menuett in C, K.1f

7 Menuett in F, K.2

8 Allegro in B flat, K.3

9 Menuett in F, K.4

10 Menuett in F, K.5

11 Allegro in C, K.5a

From the LONDON NOTEBOOK, 1764–5

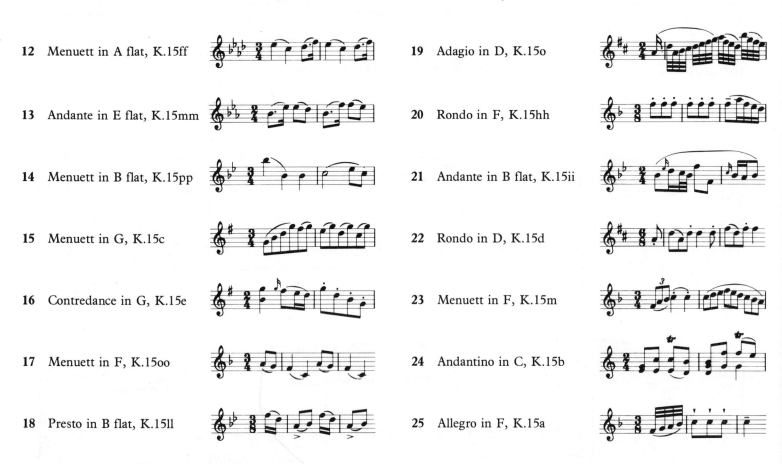

12 Menuett in A flat, K.15ff

13 Andante in E flat, K.15mm

14 Menuett in B flat, K.15pp

15 Menuett in G, K.15c

16 Contredance in G, K.15e

17 Menuett in F, K.15oo

18 Presto in B flat, K.15ll

19 Adagio in D, K.15o

20 Rondo in F, K.15hh

21 Andante in B flat, K.15ii

22 Rondo in D, K.15d

23 Menuett in F, K.15m

24 Andantino in C, K.15b

25 Allegro in F, K.15a